Lili's
Breakfast

On Monday,
Mom made toast for Lili.

"Can I have two big rectangles,
please?" said Lili.

Mom cut the toast
into two big rectangles.

On Tuesday,
Mom made toast for Lili.

"Can I have two big triangles,
please?" said Lili.

Mom cut the toast
into two big triangles.

On Wednesday,
Mom made toast for Lili.

"Can I have four little triangles,
please?" said Lili.

Mom cut the toast
into four little triangles.

On Thursday,
Mom made toast for Lili.

"Can I have four little squares,
please?" said Lili.

Mom cut the toast
into four little squares.

On Friday,
Mom made toast for Lili.

"Can I have one big square,
please?" said Lili.

Mom did not cut the toast.
It was one big square.

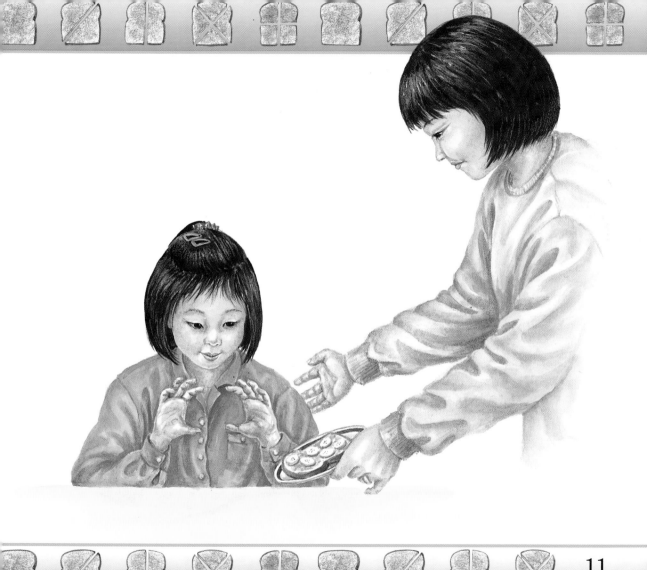

On Saturday morning,
Mom stayed in bed.
Lili made the toast.

She made rectangles.
She made triangles.
She made squares.

Then she got into bed with Mom
and helped her eat the toast!